1935...

read a g...
either a lot ... ...oney or a library card.
Cheap paperbacks were available, but their
poor production generally mirrored the quality
between the covers. One weekend that year,
Allen Lane, Managing Director of The Bodley Head,
having spent the weekend visiting Agatha Christie,
found himself on a platform at Exeter station trying to
find something to read for his journey back to London.
He was appalled by the quality of the material he had to
choose from. Everything that Allen Lane achieved from that
day until his death in 1970 was based on a passionate belief
in the existence of 'a vast reading public for *intelligent*
books at a low price'. The result of his momentous vision
was the birth not only of Penguin, but of the 'paperback
revolution'. Quality writing became available for the price of
a packet of cigarettes, literature became a mass medium
for the first time, a nation of book-borrowers became a
nation of book-buyers – and the very concept of book
publishing was changed for ever. Those founding
principles – of quality and value, with an overarching
belief in the fundamental importance of reading –
have guided everything the company has
done since 1935. Sir Allen Lane's
pioneering spirit is still very much alive
at Penguin in 2005. Here's to
the next 70 years!

MORE THAN A BUSINESS

'We decided it was time to end the almost customary half-hearted manner in which cheap editions were produced – as though the only people who could possibly want cheap editions must belong to a lower order of intelligence. We, however, believed in the existence in this country of a vast reading public for intelligent books at a low price, and staked everything on it'
Sir Allen Lane, 1902–1970

'The Penguin Books are splendid value for sixpence, so splendid that if other publishers had any sense they would combine against them and suppress them'
George Orwell

'More than a business ... a national cultural asset'
Guardian

'When you look at the whole Penguin achievement you know that it constitutes, in action, one of the more democratic successes of our recent social history'
Richard Hoggart

Hotheads

STEVEN PINKER

PENGUIN BOOKS

PENGUIN BOOKS

Published by the Penguin Group
Penguin Books Ltd, 80 Strand, London WC2R ORL, England
Penguin Group (USA) Inc., 375 Hudson Street, New York, New York 10014, USA
Penguin Group (Canada), 10 Alcorn Avenue, Toronto, Ontario, Canada M4V 3B2
(a division of Pearson Penguin Canada Inc.)
Penguin Ireland, 25 St Stephen's Green, Dublin 2, Ireland
(a division of Penguin Books Ltd)
Penguin Group (Australia), 250 Camberwell Road, Camberwell, Victoria 3124,
Australia (a division of Pearson Australia Group Pty Ltd)
Penguin Books India Pvt Ltd, 11 Community Centre,
Panchsheel Park, New Delhi – 110 017, India
Penguin Group (NZ), cnr Airborne and Rosedale Roads, Albany,
Auckland 1310, New Zealand (a division of Pearson New Zealand Ltd)
Penguin Books (South Africa) (Pty) Ltd, 24 Sturdee Avenue,
Rosebank 2196, South Africa

Penguin Books Ltd, Registered Offices: 80 Strand, London WC2R ORL, England

www.penguin.com

How the Mind Works first published in the USA by W. W. Norton 1997
Published in Penguin Books 1999
This extract published as a Pocket Penguin 2005

1

Copyright © Steven Pinker, 1997
All rights reserved

The moral right of the author has been asserted

Set in 11/13pt Monotype Dante
Typeset by Palimpsest Book Production Limited
Polmont, Stirlingshire
Printed in England by Clays Ltd, St Ives plc

The Happiness Treadmill

The pursuit of happiness is an inalienable right, says the Declaration of Independence in its list of self-evident truths. The greatest happiness of the greatest number, wrote Jeremy Bentham, is the foundation of morality. To say that everyone wants to be happy sounds trite, almost circular, but it raises a profound question about our makeup. What is this thing that people strive for?

At first happiness might seem like just desserts for biological fitness (more accurately, the states that would have led to fitness in the environment in which we evolved). We are happier when we are healthy, well-fed, comfortable, safe, prosperous, knowledgeable, respected, non-celibate, and loved. Compared to their opposites, these objects of striving are conducive to reproduction. The function of happiness would be to mobilize the mind to seek the keys to Darwinian fitness. When we are unhappy, we work for the things that make us happy; when we are happy, we keep the status quo.

The problem is, how much fitness is worth striving for? Ice Age people would have been wasting their time if they had fretted about their lack of camping stoves, penicillin, and hunting rifles or if they had striven for them instead of better caves and spears. Even among modern foragers, very different standards of living are attainable in different times and places. Lest the perfect be the enemy of the good, the pursuit of happiness ought to be calibrated by what can be attained through reasonable effort in the current environment.

How do we know what can reasonably be attained? A good source of information is what other people have attained. If they can get it, perhaps so can you. Through the ages, observers of the human condition have pointed out the tragedy: people are happy when they feel better off than their neighbors, unhappy when they feel worse off.

> But, O! how bitter a thing it is to look
> into happiness through another man's eyes!
> – William Shakespeare (*As You Like It*, V, ii).

> **Happiness**, n. An agreeable sensation arising
> from contemplating the misery of others.
> – Ambrose Bierce

> It is not enough to succeed. Others must fail.
> – Gore Vidal

> Ven frait zich a hoiker? Ven er zet a gresseren
> hoiker far zich. (When does a hunchback rejoice?
> When he sees one with a larger hump.)
> – Yiddish saying

Research on the psychology of happiness has borne out the curmudgeons. Kahneman and Tversky give an everyday example. You open your paycheck and are delighted to find you have been given a five percent raise

– until you learn that your co-workers have been given a ten percent raise. According to legend, the diva Maria Callas stipulated that any opera house she sang in had to pay her one dollar more than the next highest paid singer in the company.

People today are safer, healthier, better fed, and longer-lived than at any time in history. Yet we don't spend our lives walking on air, and presumably our ancestors were not chronically glum. It is not reactionary to point out that many of the poor in today's Western nations live in conditions that yesterday's aristocrats could not have dreamed of. People in different classes and countries are often content with their lot until they compare themselves to the more affluent. The amount of violence in a society is more closely related to its inequality than to its poverty. In the second half of the twentieth century, the discontent of the Third World, and later the Second, have been attributed to their glimpses through the mass media of the First.

The other major clue to the attainable is how well off you are now. What you have now is attainable, by definition, and chances are you can do at least a little bit better. Evolutionary theory predicts that a man's reach should exceed his grasp, but not by much. Here we have the second tragedy of happiness: people adapt to their circumstances, good or bad, the way their eyes adapt to sun or darkness. From that neutral point, improvement is happiness, loss is misery. Again, the sages said it first. The narrator of E. A. Robinson's poem (and later Simon and Garfunkel's song) envies the factory owner, Richard Cory, who 'glittered when he walked.'

So on we worked, and waited for the light,
And went without the meat, and cursed the bread;
And Richard Cory, one calm summer night,
Went home and put a bullet through his head.

The futility of striving has led many dark souls to deny that happiness is possible. For the show-business personality Oscar Levant, 'Happiness is not something you experience, it's something you remember.' Freud said that the goal of psychotherapy was 'to transform hysterical misery into common unhappiness.' A colleague, consulting with me by email about a troubled graduate student, wrote, 'sometimes i wish i was young then i remember that wasn't so great either.'

But here the curmudgeons are only partly right. People do come to feel the same across an astonishing range of good and bad fortunes. But the baseline that people adapt to, on average, is not misery but satisfaction. (The exact baseline differs from person to person and is largely inherited.) The psychologists David Myers and Ed Diener have found that about eighty percent of people in the industrialized world report that they are at least 'fairly satisfied with life,' and about thirty percent say they are 'very happy.' (As far as we can tell, the reports are sincere.) The percentages are the same for all ages, for both sexes, for blacks and whites, and over four decades of economic growth. As Myers and Diener remark, 'Compared with 1957, Americans have twice as many cars per person – plus microwave ovens, color TVs. VCRs, air conditioners, answering machines, and $12 billion worth of new brand-name athletic shoes a year. So, are Americans happier than they were in 1957? They are not.'

Within an industrialized country, money buys only a little happiness: the correlation between wealth and satisfaction is positive but small. Lottery winners, after their jolt of happiness has subsided, return to their former emotional state. On the brighter side, so do people who have suffered terrible losses, such as paraplegics and survivors of the Holocaust.

These findings do not necessarily contradict the singer Sophie Tucker when she said, 'I have been poor and I have been rich. Rich is better.' In India and Bangladesh, wealth predicts happiness much better than it does in the West. Among twenty-four Western European and American nations, the higher the gross national product per capita, the happier the citizens (though there are many explanations). Myers and Diener point out that wealth is like health: not having it makes you miserable, but having it does not guarantee happiness.

The tragedy of happiness has a third act. There are twice as many negative emotions (fear, grief, anxiety, and so on) as positive ones, and losses are more keenly felt than equivalent gains. The tennis star Jimmy Connors once summed up the human condition: 'I hate to lose more than I like to win.' The asymmetry has been confirmed in the lab by showing that people will take a bigger gamble to avoid a sure loss than to improve on a sure gain, and by showing that people's mood plummets more when imagining a loss in their lives (for example, in course grades, or in relationships with the opposite sex) than it rises when imagining an equivalent gain. The psychologist Timothy Ketelaar notes that happiness tracks the effects of resources on biological fitness. As things get better, increases in fitness show diminishing returns: more food is better, but only up to a point. But as things get worse, decreases in fitness can take you out of the game: not enough food, and you're dead. There are many ways to become infinitely worse off (from an infection, starvation, getting eaten, a fall, ad infinitum) and not many ways to become vastly better off. That makes prospective losses more worthy of attention than gains; there are more things that make us unhappy than things that make us happy.

Donald Campbell, an early evolutionary psychologist who studied the psychology of pleasure, described humans as being on a 'hedonic treadmill,' where gains in well-being leave us no happier in the long run. Indeed, the study of happiness often sounds like a sermon for traditional values. The numbers show that it is not the rich, privileged, robust, or good-looking who are happy; it is those who have spouses, friends, religion, and challenging, meaningful work. The findings can be overstated, because they apply to averages, not individuals, and because cause and effect are hard to tease apart: being married might make you happy, but being happy might help you get and stay married. But Campbell echoed millennia of wise men and women when he summed up the research: 'The direct pursuit of happiness is a recipe for an unhappy life.'

The Sirens' Song

When we say that someone is led by emotion rather than reason, we often mean that the person sacrifices long-term interests for short-term gratification. Losing one's temper, surrendering to a seducer, blowing one's paycheck, and turning tail at the dentist's door are examples. What makes us so short-sighted?

The ability to defer a reward is called self-control or delay of gratification. Social scientists often treat it as a sign of intelligence, of the ability to anticipate the future and plan accordingly. But discounting the future, as economists call it, is part of the logic of choice for any agent that lives longer than an instant. Going for the quick reward instead of a distant payoff is often the rational strategy.

Which is better, a dollar now or a dollar a year from now? (Assume there is no inflation.) A dollar now, you might say, because you can invest it and have more than a dollar in a year. Unfortunately, the explanation is circular: the reason that interest exists in the first place is to pay people to give up the dollar that they would rather have now than a year from now. But economists point out that even if the explanation is misplaced, the answer is right: now really *is* better. First, a dollar now is available if a pressing need or opportunity arises in less than a year. Second, if you forgo the dollar now, you have no guarantee that you will get it back a year from now. Third, you might die within a year and never get to enjoy it. It is rational, therefore, to discount the future: to consume a resource now unless investing it brings a high enough return. The interest rate you should demand depends on how important the money is to you now, how likely you are to get it back, and how long you expect to live.

The struggle to reproduce is a kind of economy, and all organisms; even plants, must 'decide' whether to use resources now or save them for the future. Some of these decisions are made by the body. We grow frail with age because our genes discount the future and build strong young bodies at the expense of weak old ones. The exchange pays off over the generations because an accident may cause the body to die before it gets old, in which case any sacrifice of vigor for longevity would have gone to waste. But most decisions about the future are made by the mind. At every moment we choose, consciously or unconsciously, between good things now and better things later.

Sometimes the rational decision is 'now,' particularly when, as the saying go, life is short or there is no tomorrow. The logic is laid bare in firing-squad jokes. The condemned man is offered the ceremonial last cigarette and responds, 'No thanks, I'm trying to quit.' We laugh because we know it is pointless for him to delay gratification. Another old joke makes it clear why playing it safe is not always called for. Murray and Esther, a middle-aged Jewish couple, are touring South America. One day Murray inadvertently photographs a secret military installation, and soldiers hustle the couple off to prison. For three weeks they are tortured in an effort to get them to name their contacts in the liberation movement. Finally they are hauled in front of a military court, charged with espionage, and sentenced to death by firing squad. The next morning they are lined up in front of the wall and the sergeant asks them if they have any last requests. Esther wants to know if she can call her daughter in Chicago. The sergeant says that's not possible, and turns to Murray. 'This is crazy,' Murray shouts, 'we're not spies!' and he spits in the sergeant's face. 'Murray!' Esther cries. 'Please! Don't make trouble!'

Most of the time we are pretty sure that we will not die in minutes. But we all die sometime, and we all risk forgoing the opportunity to enjoy something if we defer it too long. In our ancestors' nomadic lifestyle, without an ability to accumulate possessions or to count on long-lived social institutions like depositors' insurance, the payoffs for consumption must have been even higher. But even if they were not, *some* urge to indulge now had to have been built into our emotions. Most likely, we evolved a mechanism to estimate our longevity and the opportunities and risks posed by different choices (eating now or later, setting up camp or pushing on) and to tune the emotions accordingly.

The political scientist James Q. Wilson and the psychologist Richard Hermstein have pointed out that many criminals act as if they discount the future steeply. A crime is a gamble whose payoff is immediate and whose possible cost comes later. They attributed the discounting to low intelligence. The psychologists Martin Daly and Margo Wilson have a different explanation. In the American inner cities, life expectancy for young males is low, and they know it. (In *Hoop Dreams*, the documentary about aspiring basketball players in a Chicago ghetto, there is an arresting scene in which the mother of one of the boys rejoices that he is alive on his eighteenth birthday.) Moreover, the social order and long-term ownership rights which would guarantee that investments are repaid are tenuous. These are precisely the circumstances in which steeply discounting the future – taking risks, consuming rather than investing – is adaptive.

More puzzling is *myopic* discounting: the tendency in all of us to prefer a large late reward to a small early one, but then to flip our preference as time passes and both rewards draw nearer. A familiar example is deciding before dinner to skip dessert (a small early reward) in order to lose weight (a large late one), but succumbing to temptation when the waiter takes the dessert orders. Myopic discounting is easy to produce in the lab: give people (or pigeons, for that matter) two buttons, one delivering a small reward now, the other delivering a larger reward later, and the subject will flip from choosing the large reward to choosing the small reward as the small one becomes imminent. The weakness of the will is an unsolved problem in economics and psychology alike. The economist Thomas Schelling asks a question about the 'rational consumer' that can also be posed of the adapted mind:

How should we conceptualize this rational consumer whom all of us know and who some of us are, who in self-disgust grinds his cigarettes down the disposal swearing that this time he means never again to risk orphaning his children with lung cancer and is on the street three hours later looking for a store that's still open to buy cigarettes; who eats a high-calorie lunch knowing that he will regret it, does regret it, cannot understand how he lost control, resolves to compensate with a low-calorie dinner, eats a high-calorie dinner knowing he will regret it, and does regret it; who sits glued to the TV knowing that again tomorrow he'll wake early in a cold sweat unprepared for that morning meeting on which so much of his career depends; who spoils the trip to Disneyland by losing his temper when his children do what he knew they were going to do when he resolved not to lose his temper when they did it?

Schelling notes the strange ways in which we defeat our self-defeating behavior: putting the alarm clock across the room so we won't turn it off and fall back to sleep, authorizing our employers to put part of each paycheck away for retirement, placing tempting snacks out of reach, setting our watches five minutes ahead. Odysseus had his crewmates plug their ears with wax and tie him to the mast so he could hear the Sirens' alluring song and not steer the ship toward them and onto the rocks.

Though myopic discounting remains unexplained, Schelling captures something important about its psychology when he roots the paradox of self-control in the modularity of the mind. He observes that 'people behave sometimes as if they had two selves, one who wants clean lungs and long life and another who adores tobacco, or one who wants a lean body and another who wants dessert, or one who yearns to improve himself by reading Adam Smith on self-command . . . and another who would rather watch an old movie on television. The two are in continual contest for control.' When the spirit is willing but the flesh is weak, such as in pondering a diet-busting dessert, we can feel two very different kinds of motives fighting within us, one responding to sights and smells, the other to doctors' advice. What about when the rewards are of the same kind, like a dollar today versus two dollars tomorrow? Perhaps an imminent reward engages a circuit for dealing with sure things and a distant one a circuit for betting on an uncertain future. One outranks the other, as if the whole person was designed to believe that a bird in the hand is worth two in the bush. In the modern environment, with its reliable knowledge of the future, that often leads to irrational choices. But our ancestors might have done well to distinguish between what is definitely enjoyable now and what is conjectured or rumored to be more enjoyable tomorrow. Even today, the delay of gratification is sometimes punished because of the frailty of human knowledge. Retirement funds go bankrupt, governments break promises, and doctors announce that everything they said was bad for you is good for you and vice versa.

I and Thou

Our most ardent emotions are evoked not by landscapes, spiders, roaches, or dessert, but by other people. Some emotions, such as anger, make us want to harm people; others, such as love, sympathy, and gratitude, make us want to help them. To understand these emotions, we first have to understand why organisms should be designed to help or to hurt one another.

Having seen nature documentaries, you may believe that wolves weed out the old and weak deer to keep the herd healthy, that lemmings commit suicide to prevent the population from starving, or that stags ram into each other for the right to breed so that the fittest individuals may perpetuate the species. The underlying assumption – that animals act for the good of the eco-system, the population, or the species – seems to follow from Darwin's theory. If in the past there were ten populations of lemmings, nine with selfish lemmings who ate their groups into starvation and one in which some died so that others might live, the tenth group would survive and today's lemmings should be willing to make the ultimate sacrifice. The belief is widespread. Every psychologist who has written about the function of the social emotions has talked about their benefit to the group.

When people say that animals act for the good of

the group, they seem not to realize that the assumption is in fact a radical departure from Darwinism and almost certainly wrong. Darwin wrote, 'Natural selection will never produce in a being any structure more injurious than beneficial to that being, for natural selection acts solely by and for the good of each.' Natural selection could select groups with selfless members only if each group could enforce a pact guaranteeing that all their members stayed selfless. But without enforcement, nothing could prevent a mutant or immigrant lemming from thinking, in effect, 'To heck with this! I'll let everyone *else* jump off the cliff, and then enjoy the food they leave behind.' The selfish lemming would reap the rewards of the others' selflessness without paying any costs himself. With that advantage, his descendants would quickly take over the population, even if the population as a whole was worse off. And that is the fate of any tendency toward sacrifice. Natural selection is the cumulative effect of the relative successes of different replicators. That means that it selects for the replicators that replicate best, namely, the selfish ones.

The inescapable fact that adaptations benefit the replicator was first articulated by the biologist George Williams and later amplified by Richard Dawkins in *The Selfish Gene*. Almost all evolutionary biologists now accept the point, though there are debates over other issues. Selection among groups is possible on paper, but most biologists doubt that the special circumstances that let it happen are ever found in the real world. Selection among branches of the tree of life is possible, but that has nothing to do with whether organisms are designed for unselfishness. Animals just don't care what happens to their group, species, or ecosystem. Wolves catch the old and weak deer because they are the easiest to catch. Hungry lemmings set out for better feeding grounds and sometimes fall or drown by accident, not suicide. Stags fight because each wants to breed, and one concedes when defeat is inevitable, or as part of a strategy that works on average against others playing the same strategy. Males who fight are wasteful to the group – indeed, males *in general* are wasteful to the group when they make up half of it, because a few studs could sire the next generation without eating half the food.

Biologists often describe these acts as self-interested behavior, but what causes behaviour is the activity of the brain, especially the circuitry for emotions and other feelings. Animals behave selfishly because of how their emotion circuits are wired. My full stomach, my warmth, my orgasms, feel better to me than yours do, and I want mine, and will seek mine, more than yours. Of course, one animal cannot directly feel what's in another one's stomach, but it could feel it indirectly by observing the second animal's behavior. So it is an interesting psychological fact that animals usually don't experience other animals' observable well-being as their own pleasure. It is an even more interesting fact that they sometimes do.

Earlier I said that natural selection selects selfish replicators. If organisms were replicators, all organisms should be selfish. But organisms do not replicate. Your parents did not replicate when they had you, because you are not identical to either of them. The blueprint that made you – your set of genes – is not the same as the blueprint that made them. Their genes were shuffled, randomly sampled to make sperm and eggs, and combined with each other's during fertilization to create a new combination of genes and a new organism unlike them. The only things that actually replicated were the genes and fragments of genes whose copies made it into you, some of which you will in turn pass down to your children, and so on. In fact, even if your mother had cloned herself, she would not have replicated; only her genes would have. That is because any changes she underwent in her lifetime – losing a finger, acquiring a tattoo, having her nose pierced – were not passed on to you. The only change you could have inherited was a mutation of one of the genes in the egg that was to become you. Genes, not bodies, replicate, and that means that genes, not bodies, should be selfish.

DNA, of course, has no feelings; 'selfish' means 'acting in ways that make one's own replication more likely.' The way for a gene to do that in an animal with a brain is to wire the brain so that the animal's pleasures and pains cause it to act in ways that lead to more copies of the gene. Often that means causing an animal to enjoy the states that make it survive and reproduce. A full belly is satisfying because full bellies keep animals alive and moving and reproducing, leading to more copies of the genes that build brains that make full bellies feel satisfying.

By building a brain that makes eating fun, a gene helps to spread copies of itself lying in the animal's gonads. The actual DNA that helps build a brain, of course, doesn't itself get passed into the egg or sperm; only the copies of the gene inside the gonads do. But here is an important twist. The genes in an animal's gonads are not the *only* extant copies of the brain-building genes; they are merely the most convenient ones for the brain-building gene to help replicate. *Any* copy capable of replicating, anywhere in the world, is a legitimate target, if it can be identified and if steps can be taken to help it replicate. A gene that worked to replicate copies of itself inside some *other* animal's gonads could do as well as a gene that worked to replicate copies of itself inside *its own* animal's gonads. As far as the gene is concerned, a copy is a copy; which animal houses it is irrelevant. To a brain-building gene, the only thing special about that animal's gonads is the *certainty* that copies of the gene will be found in those gonads (the certainty comes from the fact that the cells in an animal's body are genetic clones). That is why the brain-building genes make animals enjoy their own well-being so much. If a gene could build a brain that could tell when copies of itself were sitting in *another* animal's gonads, it would make the brain enjoy the *other* animal's well-being, and make it act in ways that increased that other animal's well-being.

When does a copy of a gene in one animal also sit inside another? When the animals are related. In most animals there is a one-in-two chance that any gene in a parent will have a copy lying inside its offspring, because offspring get half their genes from each parent. There is also a one-in-two chance that a copy is lying inside a full sibling, because full siblings inherit their genes from the same pair of parents. There is a one-in-eight chance that a copy is lying inside a first cousin, and so on. A gene that built a brain that made its owner help its relatives would indirectly help to replicate itself. The biologist William Hamilton noted that if the benefit to the relative, multiplied by the probability that a gene is shared, exceeds the cost to the animal, that gene would spread in the population. Hamilton developed and formalized an idea that had been entertained by several other biologists as well, most famously in a wise-crack by the biologist J. B. S. Haldane when he was asked if he would lay down his life for his brother. 'No,' he said, 'but for two brothers or eight cousins.'

When an animal behaves to benefit another animal at a cost to itself, biologists call it altruism. When altruism evolves because the altruist is related to the beneficiary so the altruism-causing gene benefits itself, they call it kin selection. But when we look into the psychology of the animal doing the behaving, we can give the phenomenon another name: love.

The essence of love is feeling pleasure in another's well-being and pain in its harm. These feelings motivate acts that benefit the loved one, like nurturing, feeding, and protecting. We now understand why many animals, including humans, love their children, parents, grandparents, grandchildren, siblings, aunts, uncles, nephews, nieces, and cousins: people helping relatives equals genes helping themselves. The sacrifices made for love are modulated by the degree of relatedness: people make more sacrifices for their children than for their nephews and nieces. They are modulated by the expected reproductive life of the beneficiary: parents sacrifice more for children, who have a longer life ahead of them, than children sacrifice for parents. And they are modulated by the beneficiary's own feelings of love. People love their grandmothers not because their grandmothers are expected to reproduce, but because their grandmothers love *them*, and love the rest of their family. That is, you help people who enjoy helping you and helping your relatives. That is also why men and women fall in love. The other parent of my child has as much of a genetic stake in the child as I do, so what is good for her is good for me.

Many people think that the theory of the selfish gene says that 'animals try to spread their genes.' That misstates the facts and it misstates the theory. Animals, including most people, know nothing about genetics and care even less. People love their children not because they want to spread their genes (consciously or unconsciously) but because they can't help it. That love makes them try to keep their children warm, fed, and safe. What is selfish is not the real motives of the person but the metaphorical motives of the genes that built the person. Genes 'try' to spread *themselves* by wiring animals' brains so the animals love their kin and try to keep warm, fed, and safe.

The confusion comes from thinking of people's genes as their true self, and the motives of their genes as their deepest, truest, unconscious motives. From there it's easy to draw the cynical and incorrect moral that all love is hypocritical. That confuses the real motives of the person with the metaphorical motives of the genes. Genes are not puppetmasters; they acted as the recipe for making the brain and body and then they got out of the way. They live in a parallel universe, scattered among bodies, with their own agendas.

Most discussions of the biology of altruism are really not about the biology of altruism. It's easy to see why nature documentaries, with their laudable conservationist ethic, disseminate the agitprop that animals act in the interests of the group. One subtext is, Don't hate the wolf that just ate Bambi; he's acting for the greater good. The other is, Protecting the environment is nature's way; we humans had better shape up. The opposing theory of the selfish gene has been bitterly attacked out of the fear that it vindicates the philosophy of Gordon Gekko in *Wall Street*: greed is good, greed works. Then there are those who believe in selfish genes but urge us to face up to the sad truth: at heart, Mother Teresa is really selfish.

I think moralistic science is bad for morals and bad for science. Surely paving Yosemite is unwise, Gordon Gekko is bad, and Mother Teresa is good regardless of what came out in the latest biology journals. But I suppose it is only human to feel a *frisson* when learning about what made us what we are. So I offer a more hopeful way of reflecting on the selfish gene.

The body is the ultimate barrier to empathy. Your toothache simply does not hurt me the way it hurts you. But genes are not imprisoned in bodies; the same gene lives in the bodies of many family members at once. The dispersed copies of a gene call to one another by endowing bodies with emotions. Love, compassion, and empathy are invisible fibers that connect genes in different bodies. They are the closest we will ever come to feeling someone else's toothache. When a parent wishes she could take the place of a child about to undergo surgery, it is not the species or the group or her body that wants her to have that most unselfish emotion; it is her selfish genes.

Animals are nice not just to their relatives. The biologist Robert Trivers developed a suggestion from George Williams on how another kind of altruism could evolve (where altruism, again, is defined as behavior that benefits another organism at a cost to the behaver). Dawkins explains it with a hypothetical example. Imagine a species of bird that suffers from a disease-carrying tick and must spend a good deal of time removing them with its beak. It can reach every part of its body but the top of its head. Every bird would benefit if some other bird groomed its head. If the birds in a group all responded to the sight of a head presented to them by grooming it, the group would prosper. But what would happen if a mutant presented its head for grooming but never groomed anyone else? These freeloaders would be parasite-free, *and* could use the time they saved not grooming others to look for food. With that advantage they would eventually dominate the population, even if it made the group more vulnerable to extinction. The psychologist Roger Brown explains, 'One can imagine a pathetic final act in which all birds on stage present to one another heads that none will groom.'

But say a different, grudge-bearing mutant arose. This mutant groomed strangers, groomed birds that in the past had groomed it, but refused to groom birds that had refused to groom it. Once a few of them had gained a toehold, these grudgers could prosper, because they would groom one another and not pay the costs of grooming the cheaters. And once they were established, neither indiscriminate groomers nor cheaters could drive them out, though in some circumstances cheaters could lurk as a minority.

The example is hypothetical, illustrating how altruism among non-kin – what Trivers called reciprocal altruism – can evolve. It is easy to confuse the thought experiment with a real observation; Brown remarks, 'When I have used the example in teaching, it has sometimes come back to me on exams as a real bird, often as "Skinner's pigeons," sometimes the black-headed gull, and once the robin.' Some species do practice reciprocal altruism, but not many, because it evolves only under special conditions. An animal must be able to grant a large benefit to another at a small cost to itself, and the roles must commonly reverse. The animals must devote part of their brains to recognizing each other as individuals, and, if repayment comes long after the favor, to remembering who helped them and who refused, and to deciding how to grant and withhold favors accordingly.

Humans are, of course, a brainy species, and are zoologically unusual in how often they help unrelated individuals. Our lifestyles and our minds are particularly adapted to the demands of reciprocal altruism. People have food, tools, help, and information to trade. With language, information is an ideal trade good because its cost to the giver – a few seconds of breath – is minuscule compared with the benefit to the recipient. Humans are obsessed with individuals and the human mind is equipped with goal-setting demons that regulate the doling out of favors; as with kin-directed altruism, reciprocal altruism is behaviorist shorthand for a set of thoughts and emotions. Trivers and the biologist Richard Alexander have shown how the demands of reciprocal altruism are probably the source of many human emotions. Collectively they make up a large part of the moral sense.

The minimal equipment is a cheater-detector and a tit-for-tat strategy that begrudges a gross cheater further help. A gross cheater is one who refuses to reciprocate at all, or who returns so little that the altruist gets back less than the cost of the initial favor. It has been shown that people do reason unusually well about cheaters. But the real intrigue begins with Trivers' observation that there is a more subtle way to cheat. A subtle cheater reciprocates enough to make it worth the altruist's while, but returns less than he is capable of giving, or less than the altruist would give if the situation were reversed. That puts the altruist in an awkward position. In one sense she is being ripped off. But if she insists on equity, the subtle cheater could break off the relationship altogether. Since half a loaf is better than none, the altruist is trapped. She does have one kind of leverage, though. If there are *other* trading partners in the group who don't cheat at all, or who cheat subtly but less stingily, she can give them her business instead.

The game has become more complicated. Selection favors cheating when the altruist will not find out or when she will not break off her altruism if she does find out. That leads to better cheater-detectors, which leads to more subtle cheating, which leads to detectors for more subtle cheating, which leads to tactics to get away with subtle cheating without being detected by the subtle-cheater-detectors, and so on. Each detector must trigger an emotion demon that sets up the appropriate goal – continuing to reciprocate, breaking off the relationship, and so on.

Here is how Trivers reverse-engineered the moralistic emotions as strategies in the reciprocity game. (His assumptions about the causes and consequences of each emotion are well supported by the literature in experimental social psychology and by studies of other cultures, though they are hardly necessary, as real-life examples no doubt will flood into mind.)

Liking is the emotion that initiates and maintains an altruistic partnership. It is, roughly, a willingness to offer someone a favor, and is directed to those who appear willing to offer favors back. We like people who are nice to us, and we are nice to people whom we like.

Anger protects a person whose niceness has left her vulnerable to being cheated. When the exploitation is discovered, the person classifies the offending act as unjust and experiences indignation and a desire to respond with moralistic aggression: punishing the cheater by severing the relationship and sometimes by hurting him. Many psychologists have remarked that anger has moral overtones; almost all anger is righteous anger. Furious people feel they are aggrieved and must redress an injustice.

Gratitude calibrates the desire to reciprocate according to the costs and benefits of the original act. We are grateful to people when their favor helps us a lot and has cost them a lot.

Sympathy, the desire to help those in need, may be an emotion for earning gratitude. If people are most grateful when they most need the favor, a person in need is an opportunity to make an altruistic act go farthest.

Guilt can rack a cheater who is in danger of being found out. H. L. Mencken defined *conscience* as 'the inner voice which warns us that someone might be looking.' If the victim responds by cutting off all future aid, the cheater will have paid dearly. He has an interest in preventing the rupture by making up for the misdeed and keeping it from happening again. People feel guilty about private transgressions because they may become public; confessing a sin before it is discovered is evidence of sincerity and gives the victim better grounds to maintain the relationship. *Shame*, the reaction to a transgression after it has been discovered, evokes a public display of contrition, no doubt for the same reason.

Lily Tomlin said, 'I try to be cynical, but it's hard to keep up.' Trivers notes that once these emotions evolved, people had an incentive to mimic them to take advantage of other people's reactions to the real thing.

Sham generosity and friendship may induce genuine altruism in return. Sham moral anger when no real cheating took place may nonetheless win reparations. Sham guilt may convince a wronged party that the cheater has reformed his ways, even if cheating is about to resume. Feigning dire straits may evoke genuine sympathy. Sham sympathy which gives the appearance of helping may elicit real gratitude. Sham gratitude may mislead an altruist into expecting a favor to be recipro-cated. Trivers notes that none of this hypocrisy need be conscious; indeed, as we shall see, it is most effective when it is not.

The next round in this evolutionary contest is, of course, developing an ability to discriminate between real emotions and sham emotions. We get the evolu-tion of *trust* and *distrust*. When we see someone going through the motions of generosity, guilt, sympathy, or gratitude rather than showing signs of the genuine emotion, we lose the desire to cooperate. For example, if a cheater makes amends in a calculating manner rather than out of credible guilt, he may cheat again when circumstances allow him to get away with it. The search for signs of trustworthiness makes us into mind readers, alert for any twitch or inconsistency that betrays a sham emotion. Since hypocrisy is easiest to expose when people compare notes, the search for trustworthi-ness makes us avid consumers of gossip. In turn, our reputation becomes our most valuable possession, and we are motivated to protect (and inflate) it with conspic-uous displays of generosity, sympathy, and integrity and to take umbrage when it is impugned.

Are you keeping up? The ability to guard against sham emotions can in turn be used as a weapon against real emotions. One can protect one's own cheating by imputing false motives to someone else – by saying that a person really isn't aggrieved, friendly, grateful, guilty, and so on, when she really is. No wonder Trivers was the first to propose that the expansion of the human brain was driven by a cognitive arms race, fueled by the emotions needed to regulate reciprocal altruism.

Like kin selection, reciprocal altruism has been condemned as painting, even condoning, a bleak picture of human motives. Is sympathy nothing but a cheap way to buy gratitude? Is niceness just a business tactic? Not at all. Go ahead and think the worst about the sham emotions. But the reason the real ones are felt is not that they are hoped to help the feeler; it is that they in fact helped the feeler's ancestors. And it's not just that you shouldn't visit the iniquities of the fathers upon the children; the fathers may never have been iniquitous to begin with. The first mutants who felt sympathy and gratitude may have prospered not by their own calculation but because the feelings made it worth their neighbors' while to cooperate with them. The emotions themselves may have been kind and heartfelt in every generation; indeed, once sham-emotion-detectors evolved, they would be most effective when they *are* kind and heartfelt. Of course, the genes are metaphorically selfish in endowing people with beneficent emotions, but who cares about the moral worth of deoxyribonucleic acid?

Many people still resist the idea that the moral emotions are designed by natural selection to further the long-term interests of individuals and ultimately their genes. Wouldn't it be better for everyone if we were built to enjoy what was best for the group? Companies wouldn't pollute, public service unions wouldn't strike, citizens would recycle bottles and take the bus, and those teenagers would stop ruining a quiet Sunday afternoon with their jet-skis.

Once again I think it is unwise to confuse how the mind works with how it would be nice for the mind to work. But perhaps some comfort may be taken in a different way of looking at things. Perhaps we should *rejoice* that people's emotions aren't designed for the good of the group. Often the best way to benefit one's group is to displace, subjugate, or annihilate the group next door. Ants in a colony are closely related, and each is a paragon of unselfishness. That's why ants are one of the few kinds of animal that wage war and take slaves. When human leaders have manipulated or coerced people into submerging their interests into the group's, the outcomes are some of history's worst atrocities. In *Love and Death*, Woody Allen's pacifist character is urged to defend the czar and Mother Russia with the dubious call to duty that under French rule he would have to eat croissants and rich food with heavy sauces. People's desire for a comfortable life for themselves, their family, and their friends may have braked the ambitions of many an emperor.

The Doomsday Machine

It is 1962, and you are the president of the United States. You have just learned that the Soviet Union has dropped an atomic bomb on New York. You know they will not attack again. In front of you is the phone to the Pentagon, the proverbial button, with which you can retaliate by bombing Moscow.

You are about to press the button. The nation's policy is to retaliate in kind against a nuclear attack. The policy was designed to deter attackers; if you don't follow through, the deterrent would have been a sham.

On the other hand, you are thinking, the damage has been done. Killing millions of Russians will not bring millions of dead Americans back to life. The bomb will add radioactive fallout to the atmosphere, harming your own citizens. And you will go down in history as one of the worst mass murderers of all time. Retaliation now would be sheer spite.

But then, it is precisely this line of thinking that emboldened the Soviets to attack. They *knew* that once the bomb fell you would have nothing to gain and much to lose by retaliating. They thought they were calling your bluff. So you had better retaliate to show them it wasn't a bluff.

But then again, what's the point of proving *now* that you weren't bluffing *then*? The present cannot affect the past. The fact remains that if you push the button, you will snuff out millions of lives for no reason.

But wait – the Soviets knew you would think it is pointless to prove you weren't bluffing after they tried to call your bluff. That's why they called your bluff. The very fact that you are thinking this way brought on the catastrophe – so you shouldn't think this way.

But not thinking this way *now* is too late . . .

You curse your freedom. Your predicament is that you have the choice to retaliate, and since retaliating is not in your interests, you may decide not to do it, exactly as the Soviets anticipated. If only you didn't *have* the choice! If only your missiles had been wired to a reliable nuclear-fireball-detector and went off automatically. The Soviets would not have dared to attack, because they would have known retaliation was certain.

This train of reasoning was taken to its logical conclusion in the novel and film *Dr. Strangelove*. A deranged American officer has ordered a nuclear bomber to attack the Soviet Union, and it cannot be recalled. The president and his advisors meet in the war room with the Soviet ambassador to persuade him, and by telephone the Soviet leader, that the imminent attack is an accident and that the Soviets should not retaliate. They learn it is too late. The Soviets had installed the Doomsday Machine: a network of underground nuclear bombs that is set off automatically if the country is attacked or if anyone tries to disarm it. The fallout will destroy all human and animal life on earth. They installed the machine because it was cheaper than pinpoint missiles and bombers, and because they feared the United States might be building one and wanted to prevent a Doomsday gap. President Muffley (played by Peter Sellers) confers with the country's top nuclear strategist, the brilliant Dr. Strangelove (played by Peter Sellers):

'But,' Muffley said, 'is it really possible for it to be triggered automatically and at the same time impossible to untrigger?'

. . . Doctor Strangelove said quickly, 'But precisely. Mister President, it is not only possible, it is essential. That is the whole idea of this machine. Deterrence is the art of producing in the enemy the fear to attack. And so because of the automated and irrevocable decision-making process which rules out human meddling, the Doomsday Machine is terrifying, simple to understand, and completely credible and convincing.' . . .

President Muffley said, 'But this is fantastic, Doctor Strangelove. How can it be triggered automatically?'

Strangelove said, 'Sir, it is remarkably simple to do that. When you merely wish to bury bombs there is no limit to the size. . . . After they are buried they are connected to a gigantic complex of computers. A specific and closely defined set of circumstances under which the bombs are to be exploded is programmed into the tape memory banks. . . .' Strangelove turned so he looked directly at [the Soviet Ambassador]. 'There is only one thing I don't understand, Mister Ambassador. The whole point of the Doomsday Machine is lost if you keep it a secret. Why didn't you tell the world?'

[The ambassador] turned away. He said quietly but distinctly, 'It was to be announced at the Party Congress on Monday. As you know, the Premier loves surprises.'

The German-accented, leather-gloved, wheelchair-bound Dr. Strangelove, with his disconcerting tic of giving the Nazi salute is one of cinema's all-time eeriest characters. He was meant to symbolize a kind of intellectual who until recently was prominent in the public's imagination: the nuclear strategist, paid to think the unthinkable. These men, who included Henry Kissinger (on whom Sellers based his portrayal), Herman Kahn, John von Neumann, and Edward Teller, were stereotyped as amoral nerds who cheerfully filled blackboards with equations about megadeaths and mutual assured destruction. Perhaps the scariest thing about them was their paradoxical conclusions – for example, that safety in the nuclear age comes from exposing one's cities and protecting one's missiles.

But the unsettling paradoxes of nuclear strategy apply to *any* conflict between parties whose interests are partly competing and partly shared. Common sense says that victory goes to the side with the most intelligence, self-interest, coolness, options, power, and clear lines of communication. Common sense is wrong. Each of these assets can be a liability in contests of strategy (as opposed to contests of chance, skill, or strength), where behavior is calculated by predicting what the other guy will do in response. Thomas Schelling has shown that the paradoxes are ubiquitous in social life. We shall see that they offer great insight into the emotions, particularly the headstrong passions that convinced the Romantics that emotion and reason were opposites. But first let's put the emotions aside and just examine the logic of conflicts of strategy.

Take bargaining. When two people haggle over a car or a house, a bargain is struck when one side makes the final concession. Why does he concede? Because he is sure she will not. The reason she won't concede is that she thinks he will concede. She thinks he will because she thinks he thinks she thinks he will. And so on. There always is a range of prices that the buyer and seller would both accept. Even if a particular price within that range is not the best price for one party, it is preferable to canceling the deal outright. Each side is vulnerable to being forced to settle for the worst acceptable price because the other side realizes that he or she would have no choice if the alternative was to reach no agreement at all. But when both parties can guess the range, *any* price within the range is a point from which at least one party would have been willing to back off, and the other party knows it.

Schelling points out that the trick to coming out ahead is 'a voluntary but irreversible sacrifice of freedom of choice.' How do you persuade someone that you will not pay more than $16,000 for a car that is really worth $20,000 to you? You can make a public, enforceable $5,000 bet with a third party that you won't pay more than $16,000. As long as $16,000 gives the dealer a profit, he has no choice but to accept. Persuasion would be futile; it's against your interests to compromise. By tying your own hands, you improve your bargaining position. The example is fanciful, but real ones abound. The dealer appoints a salesperson who is not authorized to sell at less than a certain price even if he says he wants to. A homebuyer cannot get a mortgage if the bank's appraiser says he paid too much. The homebuyer exploits that powerlessness to get a better price from the seller.

Not only can power be a liability in conflicts of strategy, communication can be, too. When you are haggling from a pay phone with a friend about where to meet for dinner, you can simply announce that you will be at Ming's at six-thirty and hang up. The friend has to accede if she wants to meet you at all.

Paradoxical tactics also enter into the logic of promises. A promise can secure a favor only when the beneficiary of the promise has good reason to believe it will be carried out. The promiser is thus in a *better* position when the beneficiary knows that the promiser is *bound* by his promise. The law gives companies the right to sue and the right to be sued. The right to be sued? What kind of 'right' is that? It is a right that confers the power to make a promise: to enter into contracts, borrow money, and engage in business with someone who might be harmed as a result. Similarly, the law that empowers banks to foreclose on a mortgage makes it worth the bank's while to grant the mortgage, and so, paradoxically, benefits the *borrower*. In some societies, Schelling notes, eunuchs got the best jobs because of what they could not do. How does a hostage persuade his kidnapper not to kill him to prevent him from identifying the kidnapper in court? One option is to deliberately blind himself. A better one is to confess to a shameful secret that the kidnapper can use as blackmail. If he has no shameful secret, he can create one by having the kidnapper photograph him in some unspeakably degrading act.

Threats, and defenses against threats, are the arena in which Dr. Strangelove really comes into his own. There are boring threats, in which the threatener has an interest in carrying out the threat – for example, when a homeowner threatens a burglar that she will call the police. The fun begins when carrying out the threat is costly to the threatener, so its value is only as a deterrent. Again, freedom is costly; the threat is credible only when the threatener has no choice but to carry it out and the target knows it. Otherwise, the target can threaten the threatener right back by refusing to comply. The Doomsday Machine is an obvious example, though the secrecy defeated its purpose. A hijacker who threatens to blow up a plane if anyone tries to disarm him will have a better chance of seeing Cuba if he wears explosives that go off with the slightest jostling. A good way to win the teenagers' game of chicken, in which two cars approach each other at high speed and the first driver to swerve loses face, is to conspicuously remove your own steering wheel and throw it away.

With threats, as with promises, communication can be a liability. The kidnapper remains incommunicado after making the ransom demand so he cannot be persuaded to give up the hostage for a smaller ransom or a safe escape. Rationality is also a liability. Schelling points out that 'if a man knocks at the back door and says that he will stab himself unless you give him $10, he is more likely to get the $10 if his eyes are bloodshot.' Terrorists, kidnappers, hijackers, and dictators of small countries have an interest in appearing mentally unbalanced. An absence of self-interest is also an advantage. Suicide bombers are almost impossible to stop.

To defend yourself *against* threats, make it impossible for the threatener to make you an offer you can't refuse. Again, freedom, information, and rationality are handicaps. 'Driver does not know combination to safe,' says the sticker on the delivery truck. A man who is worried that his daughter may be kidnapped can give away his fortune, leave town and remain incommunicado, lobby for a law that makes it a crime to pay ransom, or break the hand with which he signs checks. An invading army may burn bridges behind it to make retreat impossible. A college president tells protesters he has no influence on the town police, and genuinely wants no influence. A racketeer cannot sell protection if the customer makes sure he is not at home when the racketeer comes around.

Because an expensive threat works both ways, it can lead to a cycle of self-incapacitation. Protesters attempt to block the construction of a nuclear power plant by lying down on the railroad tracks leading to the site. The engineer, being reasonable, has no choice but to stop the train. The railroad company counters by telling the engineer to set the throttle so that the train moves very slowly and then to jump out of the train and walk beside it. The protesters must scramble. Next time the protesters handcuff themselves to the tracks; the engineer does not dare leave the train. But the protesters must be certain the engineer sees them in enough time to stop. The company assigns the next train to a nearsighted engineer.

*

In these examples, many of them from Schelling, the paradoxical power comes from a physical constraint like handcuffs or an institutional constraint like the police. But strong passions can do the same thing. Say a bargainer publicly announces that he will not pay more than $16,000 for the car, and everyone knows he could not tolerate the shame of going back on his word. The unavoidable shame is as effective as the enforceable bet, and he will get the car at his price. If Mother Teresa offered to sell you her car, you would not insist on a guarantee because presumably she is constitutionally incapable of cheating you. The hothead who can figuratively explode at any moment enjoys the same tactical advantage as the hijacker who can literally explode at any moment. In *The Maltese Falcon*. Sam Spade (Humphrey Bogart) dares the henchmen of Kasper Gutman (Sidney Greenstreet) to kill him, knowing that they need him to retrieve the falcon. Gutman replies, 'That's an attitude, sir, that calls for the most delicate judgment on both sides, because as you know, sir, in the heat of action men are likely to forget where their best interests lie, and let their emotions carry them away.' In *The Godfather*, Vito Corleone tells the heads of the other crime families, 'I'm a superstitious man. And if some unlucky accident should befall my son, if my son is struck by a bolt of lightning, I will blame some of the people here.'

Dr. Strangelove meets The Godfather. Is passion a doomsday machine? People consumed by pride, love, or rage have lost control. They may be irrational. They may act against their interests. They may be deaf to appeals. (The man running amok calls to mind a dooms-day machine that has been set off.) But though this be madness, yet there is method in it. Precisely these sacrifices of will and reason are effective tactics in the countless bargains, promises, and threats that make up our social relations.

The theory stands the Romantic model on its head. The passions are no vestige of an animal past, no well-spring of creativity, no enemy of the intellect. The intel-lect is designed to relinquish control to the passions so that they may serve as guarantors of its offers, prom-ises, and threats against suspicions that they are lowballs, double-crosses, and bluffs. The apparent firewall between passion and reason is not an ineluctable part of the architecture of the brain; it has been programmed in deliberately, because only if the passions are in control can they be credible guarantors.

The doomsday-machine theory has been proposed independently by Schelling, Trivers, Daly and Wilson, the economist Jack Hirshleifer, and the economist Robert Frank. Righteous anger, and the attendant thirst for redress or vengeance, is a credible deterrent if it is uncontrollable and unresponsive to the deterrer's costs. Such compulsions, though useful in the long run, can drive people to fight far out of proportion to the stakes. In 1982 Argentina annexed the British colony of the Falklands, desolate islands with virtually no economic or strategic importance. In earlier decades it might have made sense for Britain to defend them as an immediate deterrent to anyone with designs on the rest of its empire, but at that point there was no empire left to defend. Frank points out that for what they spent to reclaim the islands, Britain could have given each Falklander a Scottish castle and a lifetime pension. But most Britons were proud that they stood up to the Argentinians. The same sense of fairness makes us sue expensively for small amounts or seek a refund for a defective product despite red tape that costs us more in lost wages than the product was worth.

The lust for revenge is a particularly terrifying emotion. All over the world, relatives of the slain fantasize day and night about the bittersweet moment when they might avenge a life with a life and find peace at last. The emotion strikes us as primitive and dreadful because we have contracted the government to settle our scores for us. But in many societies an irresistible thirst for vengeance is one's only protection against deadly raids. Individuals may differ in the resolve with which they will suffer costs to carry out vengeance. Since that resolve is an effective deterrent only if it is advertised, it is accompanied by the emotion traditionally referred to as honor: the desire to publicly avenge even minor trespasses and insults. The hair-trigger of honor and revenge can be tuned to the degree of threat in the environment. Honor and vengeance are raised to godly virtues in societies that lie beyond the reach of law enforcement, such as remote horticulturalists and herders, the pioneers of the Wild West, street gangs, organized crime families, and entire nation-states when dealing with one another (in which case the emotion is called 'patriotism'). But even within a modern state society where it serves no purpose, the emotion of vengeance cannot easily be turned off. Most legal theories, even from the highest-minded philosophers, acknowledge that retribution is one of the legitimate goals of criminal punishment, over and above the goals of deterring potential criminals and incapacitating, deterring, and rehabilitating the offender. Enraged crime victims long disenfranchised from the American legal system, have recently pressed for a say in plea-bargaining and sentencing decisions.

As Strangelove explained, the whole point of a dooms-day machine is lost if you keep it a secret. That principle may explain one of the longest-standing puzzles of the emotions: why we advertise them on our face.

Darwin himself never argued that facial expressions were naturally selected adaptations. In fact, his theory was downright Lamarckian. Animals have to move their faces for practical reasons: they bare the teeth to bite, widen the eyes for a panoramic view, and pull back the ears to protect them in a fight. These measures turned into habits that the animal performed when it merely anticipated an event. The habits were then passed to their offspring. It may seem strange that Darwin was no Darwinian in one of his most famous books, but remember that Darwin was fighting on two fronts. He had to explain adaptations to satisfy his fellow biologists, but he also made much of pointless features and animal vestiges in humans to combat creationists, who argued that functional design was a sign of God's handiwork. If God had really designed humans from scratch, Darwin asked, why would he have installed features that are useless to us but similar to features that are useful to animals?

Many psychologists still can't understand why broadcasting ones emotional state might be beneficial. Wouldn't the proverbial smell of fear just egg on one's enemies? One psychologist has tried to revive an old idea that facial muscles are tourniquets that send more blood to the parts of the brain that have to cope with the current challenge. Aside from being hydraulically improbable, the theory cannot explain why we are more expressive when there are other people around.

But if the passionate emotions are guarantors of threats and promises, advertising is their reason for being. But here a problem arises. Remember that real emotions create a niche for sham emotions. Why whip yourself into a rage when you can *simulate* a rage, deter your enemies, and not pay the price of pursuing dangerous vengeance if it fails? Let *others* be doomsday machines, and you can reap the benefits of the terror they sow. Of course, when counterfeit facial expressions begin to drive out the real ones, people call each other's bluffs, and the facial expressions, real and fake, become worthless.

Facial expressions are useful only if they are hard to fake. As a matter of fact, they *are* hard to fake. People don't really believe that the grinning flight attendant is happy to see them. That is because a social smile is formed with a different configuration of muscles from the genuine smile of pleasure. A social smile is executed by circuits in the cerebral cortex that are under voluntary control; a smile of pleasure is executed by circuits in the limbic system and other brain systems and is involuntary. Anger, fear, and sadness, too, recruit muscles that can't be controlled voluntarily, and the genuine expressions are hard to fake, though we can pantomime an approximation. Actors must simulate facial expressions for a living, but many cannot avoid a mannered look. Some great actors, like Laurence Olivier, are highly coordinated athletes who have doggedly learned to control every muscle. Others learn method acting, inspired by Konstantin Stanislavsky, in which actors make themselves *feel* an emotion by remembering or imagining a charged experience, and the expression pops on the face reflexively.

The explanation is incomplete, because it raises another question: *why* did we never evolve the ability to control our expressions? You can't just say that it would hurt everyone if counterfeit expressions were circulated. True enough, but in a world of honest emoters the faker would prosper, so fakers should always drive out emoters. I don't know the answer, but there are obvious places to look. Zoologists worry about the same problem: how can honest animal signals, like cries, gestures, and advertisements of health, evolve in a world of would-be fakers? One answer is that honest signals can evolve if they are too expensive to fake. For example, only a healthy peacock can afford a splendiferous tail, so healthy peacocks bear the burden of a cumbersome tail as a display of conspicuous consumption that only they can afford. When the healthiest peacocks display, the less healthy ones have no choice but to follow, because if they hide their health altogether the peahens will assume the worst, namely that they are at death's door.

Is there anything about emotional expressions that

would make it inherently costly to put them under voluntary control? Here is a guess. In designing the rest of the human, natural selection had good engineering reasons to segregate the voluntary, cognitive systems from the systems that control housekeeping and physical-plant functions such as the regulation of heartbeat, breathing rate, blood circulation, sweat, tears, and saliva. None of your conscious beliefs are pertinent to how fast your heart ought to beat, so there's no point in letting you control it. In fact, it would be downright dangerous, since you might forget to pump when you got distracted, or you might try out your own harebrained ideas on what the best pulse rate should be.

Now, say selection handcuffed each emotion to a physiological control circuit, and the activity of the circuit was visible to an observer as flushing, blushing, blanching, sweating, trembling, quavering, croaking, weeping, and the facial reflexes Darwin discussed. An observer would have good reason to believe that the emotion was genuine, since a person could not fake it unless he had voluntary control of his heart and other organs. Just as the Soviets would have wanted to show everyone the wiring of the Doomsday Machine to *prove* that it was automatic and irreversible and their description of it no bluff, people might have an interest in showing everyone that an emotion is holding their body hostage and their angry words are no bluff. If so, it would explain why emotions are so intimately tied to the body, a fact that puzzled William James and a century of psychologists after him.

The handcuffing may have been easy for natural

selection, because the major human emotions seem to have grown out of evolutionary precursors (anger from fighting, fear from fleeing, and so on), each of which engaged a suite of involuntary physiological responses. (This might be the grain of truth in the Romantic and triune-brain theories: modern emotions may *exploit* the involuntariness of older reflexes, even if they did not inherit it by default.) And once the handcuffs were in place for honest emoters, everyone else would have had little choice but to don them too, like the unhealthy peacocks forced to muster tails. A chronic poker face would suggest the worst: that the emotions a person declares in word and deed are shams.

This theory is unproven, but no one can deny the phenomenon. People are vigilant for sham emotions and put the most faith in involuntary physiological give-aways. That underlies an irony of the telecommunications age. Long-distance phone service, electronic mail, faxes, and video-conferencing should have made the face-to-face business meeting obsolete. But meetings continue to be a major expense for corporations and support entire industries like hotels, airlines, and rental cars. Why do we insist on doing business in the flesh? Because we do not trust someone until we see what makes him sweat.

Fools for Love

Why does romantic love leave us bewitched, bothered, and bewildered? Could it be another paradoxical tactic like handcuffing oneself to railroad tracks? Quite possibly. Offering to spend your life and raise children with someone is the most important promise you'll ever make, and a promise is most credible when the promiser can't back out. Here is how the economist Robert Frank has reverse-engineered mad love.

Unsentimental social scientists and veterans of the singles scene agree that dating is a marketplace. People differ in their value as potential marriage partners. Almost everyone agrees that Mr. or Ms. Right should be good-looking, smart, kind, stable, funny, and rich. People shop for the most desirable person who will accept them, and that is why most marriages pair a bride and a groom of approximately equal desirability. Mate-shopping, however, is only part of the psychology of romance; it explains the statistics of mate choice, but not the final pick.

Somewhere in this world of five billion people there lives the best-looking, richest, smartest, funniest, kindest person who would settle for you. But your dream-boat is a needle in a haystack, and you may die single if you insist on waiting for him or her to show up. Staying single has costs, such as loneliness, childlessness, and playing the dating game with all its awkward drinks and dinners (and sometimes breakfasts). At some point it pays to set up house with the best person you have found so far.

But that calculation leaves your partner vulnerable. The laws of probability say that someday you will meet a more desirable person, and if you are always going for the best you can get, on that day you will dump your partner. But your partner has invested money, time, childrearing, and forgone opportunities in the relationship. If your partner was the most desirable person in the world, he or she would have nothing to worry about, because you would never want to desert. But failing that, the partner would have been foolish to enter the relationship.

Frank compares the marriage market with the rental market. Landlords desire the best of all tenants but settle for the best they can find, and renters want the best of all apartments but settle for the best they can find. Each invests in the apartment (the landlord may paint it the tenant's favorite color; the tenant may install permanent decorations), so each would be harmed if the other suddenly terminated the agreement. If the tenant could leave for a better flat, the landlord would have to bear the costs of an unrented unit and the search for a new tenant; he would have to charge a high rent to cover that risk, and would be loath to paint. If the landlord could evict the tenant for a better one, the tenant would have to search for a new home; she would be willing to pay only a low rent, and would not bother to keep the apartment in good shape, if she had to expose herself to that risk. If the best tenant were renting the best apartment, the worries would be moot; neither would want to end the arrangement. But since both have to compromise, they protect themselves by signing a lease that is expensive for either to break. By agreeing to restrict his own freedom to evict, the landlord can charge a higher rent. By agreeing to restrict her own freedom to leave, the tenant can demand a lower rent. Lack of choice works to each one's advantage.

Marriage laws work a bit like leases, but our ancestors had to find some way to commit themselves before the laws existed. How can you be sure that a prospective partner won't leave the minute it is rational to do so – say, when a 10-out-of-10 moves in next door? One answer is, don't accept a partner who wanted you for rational reasons to begin with; look for a partner who is committed to staying with you because you are you. Committed by what? Committed by an emotion. An emotion that the person did not decide to have, and so cannot decide not to have. An emotion that was not triggered by your objective mate-value and so will not be alienated by someone with greater mate-value. An emotion that is guaranteed not to be a sham because it has physiological costs like tachycardia, insomnia, and anorexia. An emotion like romantic love.

'People who are sensible about love are incapable of it,' wrote Douglas Yates. Even when courted by the perfect suitor, people are unable to will themselves to fall in love, often to the bewilderment of the matchmaker, the suitor, and the person himself or herself. Instead it is a glance, a laugh, a manner that steals the heart. We fall in love with the individual, not with the individual's qualities. The upside is that when Cupid does strike, the lovestruck one is all the more credible in the eyes of the object of desire. Murmuring that your lover's looks, earning power, and IQ meet your minimal standards would probably kill the romantic mood, even though the statement is statistically true. The way to a person's heart is to declare the opposite – that you're in love because you can't help it. Tipper Gore's Parents' Music Resource Center notwithstanding, the sneering, body-pierced, guitar-smashing rock musician is typically not singing about drugs, sex, or Satan. He is singing about love. He is courting a woman by calling attention to the irrationality, uncontrollability, and physiological costs of his desire. I want you so bad, it's driving me mad, Can't eat, can't sleep, Heart beats like a big bass drum, You're the only one, Don't know why I love you like I do, You drive me crazy, Can't stop lovin' you, Ain't nobody can do it to me the way you can, I like the way you walk, I like the way you talk, et cetera, et cetera.

Of course, one can well imagine a woman not being swept off her feet by these proclamations. (Or a man, if it is a woman doing the declaring.) They set off a warning light in the other component of coursthip, smart shopping. Groucho Marx said that he would not belong to any club that would have him as a member. Usually people do not want any suitor who wants them too badly too early, because it shows that the suitor is desperate (so they should wait for someone better), and because it shows that the suitor's ardor is too easily triggered (hence too easily triggerable by someone else). The contradiction of courtship – flaunt your desire while playing hard to get – comes from the two parts of romantic love: setting a minimal standard for candidates in the mate market, and capriciously committing body and soul to one of them.

The Society of Feelings

Mental life often feels like a parliament within. Thoughts and feelings vie for control as if each were an agent with strategies for taking over the whole person, you. Might our mental agents use paradoxical tactics with one another – handcuffs, doomsday machines, unbreakable contracts with third parties? The analogy is imperfect because natural selection designs people to compete but does not design organs, including mental agents, to compete; the interests of the whole person are paramount. But the whole person has many goals, like food, sex, and safety, and that requires a division of labor among mental agents with different priorities and kinds of expertise. The agents are bound by an entente that benefits the whole person over a lifetime, but over the short term the agents may outwit one another with devious tactics.

Self-control is unmistakably a tactical battle between parts of the mind. Schelling observes that the tactics people use to control themselves are interchangeable with the tactics they use to control others. How do you prevent your child from scratching his hives in his sleep? Put mittens on him. How do you prevent yourself from scratching your hives in your sleep? Put mittens on yourself. If Odysseus had not plugged his shipmates ears, they would have done it on their own. The self that wants a trim body outwits the self that wants dessert by throwing out the brownies at the opportune moment when it is in control.

So we do seem to use paradoxical tactics against ourselves. The agent in control at one time makes a voluntary but irreversible sacrifice of freedom of choice for the whole body, and gets its way in the long run. That is the bright spot in this whole depressing discussion of selfish genes and doomsday machines. Social life is not always the equivalent of global thermonuclear war because the part of us with the longest view of the future, when in control of the body, can voluntarily sacrifice freedom of choice for the body at other times. We sign contracts, submit to laws, and hitch our reputations to public declarations of loyalty to friends and mates. These are not tactics to defeat someone else, but tactics to defeat the darker parts of ourselves.

One more speculation on the battle inside the head. No one knows what, if anything, grief is for. Obviously the loss of a loved one is unpleasant, but why should it be devastating? Why the debilitating pain that stops people from eating, sleeping, resisting diseases, and getting on with life? Jane Goodall describes a young chimp, Flint, who after the death of his beloved mother became depressed and died himself as if of a broken heart.

Some have suggested that grief is an enforced interlude for reassessment. Life will never be the same, so one must take time to plan how to cope with a world that has been turned upside down. Perhaps grief also gives people time to contemplate how a lapse of theirs may have allowed the death and how they might be more careful in the future. There may be an element of truth to the suggestion. Bereaved people find that they ache all over again every time they discover another habit to unlearn, like setting out an extra plate or buying groceries for two. And blaming oneself is a common symptom. But the pain of grief makes planning harder, not easier, and is too extreme and long-lasting to be useful as a strategy session.

William James wrote, 'It takes a mind debauched by learning to carry the process of making the natural seem strange so far as to ask for the "why" of any instinctive human act.' Though legitimate to a scientist, the question 'Why do we grieve?' is preposterous to common sense. If you didn't grieve when someone died, could you really have loved him when he was alive? It's logically possible but seems psychologically impossible; grief is the other side of love. And there may lie the answer. Perhaps grief is an internal doomsday machine, pointless once it goes off, useful only as a deterrent. What parents have not lain awake contemplating the horror of losing a child? Or worried themselves sick with awful images when a child is late or lost? These thoughts are powerful reminders to protect and cherish a loved one in the face of myriad other demands on one's time and thoughts. Like all deterrents, grief would be effective only if it is certain and terrible.

Kidding Ourselves

The playwright Jerome K. Jerome once said, 'It is always the best policy to tell the truth, unless, of course, you are an exceptionally good liar.' It's hard to be a good liar, even when it comes to your own intentions, which only you can verify. Intentions come from emotions, and emotions have evolved displays on the face and body. Unless you are a master of the Stanislavsky method, you will have trouble faking them; in fact, they probably evolved *because* they were hard to fake. Worse, lying is stressful, and anxiety has its own telltale markers. They are the rationale for polygraphs, the so-called lie detectors, and humans evolved to be lie detectors, too. Then there is the annoying fact that some propositions logically entail others. Since *some* of the things you say will be true, you are always in danger of exposing your own lies. As the Yiddish saying goes, a liar must have a good memory.

Trivers, pursuing his theory of the emotions to its logical conclusion, notes that in a world of walking lie detectors the best strategy is to believe your own lies. You can't leak your hidden intentions if you don't think that they *are* your intentions. According to his theory of self-deception, the conscious mind sometimes hides the truth from itself the better to hide it from others. But the truth is useful, so it should be registered somewhere in the mind, walled off from the parts that interact with other people. There is an obvious similarity to Freud's theory of the unconscious and the defense mechanisms of the ego (such as repression, projection, denial, and rationalization), though the explanation is completely different. George Orwell stated it in *1984*: 'The secret of rulership is to combine a belief in one's own infallibility with a power to learn from past mistakes.'

The neuroscientist Michael Gazzaniga has shown that the brain blithely weaves false explanations about its motives. Split-brain patients have had their cerebral hemispheres surgically disconnected as a treatment for epilepsy. Language circuitry is in the left hemisphere, and the left half of the visual field is registered in the isolated right hemisphere, so the part of the split-brain person that can talk is unaware of the left half of his world. The right hemisphere is still active, though, and can carry out simple commands presented in the left visual field, like 'Walk' or 'Laugh.' When the patient (actually, the patient's left hemisphere) is asked why he walked out (which we know was a response to the command presented to the right hemisphere), he ingenuously replies, 'To get a Coke.' When asked why he is laughing, he says, 'You guys come up and test us every month. What a way to make a living!'

Our confabulations, not coincidentally, present us in the best light. Literally hundreds of experiments in social psychology say so. The humorist Garrison Keillor describes the fictitious community of Lake Wobegon, 'where the women are strong, the men are good-looking, and all the children are above average.' Indeed, most people claim they are above average in any positive trait you name: leadership, sophistication, athletic prowess, managerial ability, even driving skill. They rationalize the boast by searching for an *aspect* of the trait that they might in fact be good at. The slow drivers say they are above average in safety, the fast ones that they are above average in reflexes.

More generally, we delude ourselves about how benevolent and how effective we are, a combination that social psychologists call beneffectance. When subjects play games that are rigged by the experimenter, they attribute their successes to their own skill and their failures to the luck of the draw. When they are fooled in a fake experiment into thinking they have delivered shocks to another subject, they derogate the victim, implying that he deserved the punishment. Everyone has heard of 'reducing cognitive dissonance', in which people invent a new opinion to resolve a contradiction in their minds. For example, a person will recall enjoying a boring task if he had agreed to recommend it to others for paltry pay. (If the person had been enticed to recommend the task for generous pay, he accurately recalls that the task was boring.) As originally conceived of by the psychologist Leon Festinger, cognitive dissonance is an unsettled feeling that arises from an inconsistency in one's beliefs. But that's not right: there is no contradiction between the proposition 'The task is boring' and the proposition 'I was pressured into lying that the task was fun'. Another social psychologist, Eliot Aronson, nailed it down: people doctor their beliefs only to eliminate a contradiction with the proposition 'I am nice and in control'. Cognitive dissonance is always triggered by blatant evidence that you are not as beneficent and effective as you would like people to think. The urge to reduce it is the urge to get your self-serving story straight.

Sometimes we have glimpses of our own self-deception. When does a negative remark sting, cut deep, hit a nerve? When some part of us knows it is true. If every part knew it was true, the remark would not sting; it would be old news. If no part thought it was true, the remark would roll off; we could dismiss it as false. Trivers recounts an experience that is all too familiar (at least to me). One of his papers drew a published critique, which struck him at the time as vicious and unprincipled, full of innuendo and slander. Rereading the article years later, he was surprised to find that the wording was gentler, the doubts more reasonable, the attitude less biased than he had remembered. Many others have made such discoveries; they are almost the definition of 'wisdom'.

If there were a verb meaning 'to believe falsely,' it would not have any significant first person, present indicative.
– Ludwig Wittgenstein

There's one way to find out if a man is honest: ask him; if he says yes, you know he's crooked.
– Mark Twain

Our enemies' opinion of us comes closer to the truth than our own.
– François La Rochefoucauld

> Oh wad some power the giftie gie us
> To see oursels as ithers see us!
> – Robert Burns

No one can examine the emotions without seeing in them the source of much human tragedy. I don't think we should blame the animals; it's clear enough how natural selection engineered our instincts to suit our needs. We shouldn't blame selfish genes, either. They endow us with selfish motives, but they just as surely endow us with the capacity for love and a sense of justice. What we should appreciate and fear is the cunning designs of the emotions themselves. Many of their specs are not for gladness and understanding: think of the happiness treadmill, the Sirens' song, the sham emotions, the doomsday machines, the caprice of romance, the pointless punishment of grief. But self-deception is perhaps the cruelest motive of all, for it makes us feel right when we are wrong and emboldens us to fight when we ought to surrender. Trivers writes,

Consider an argument between two closely bound people, say, husband and wife. Both parties believe that one is an altruist – of long standing, relatively pure in motive, and much abused – while the other is characterized by a pattern of selfishness spread over hundreds of incidents. They only disagree over who is altruistic and who selfish. It is noteworthy that the argument may appear to burst forth spontaneously, with little or no preview, yet as it rolls along, two whole landscapes of information processing appear to lie already organized, waiting only for the lightning of anger to show themselves.

In cartoons and movies, the villains are mustache-twirling degenerates, cackling with glee at their badness. In real life, villains are convinced of their rectitude. Many biographers of evil men start out assuming that their subjects are cynical opportunists and reluctantly discover that they are ideologues and moralists. If Hitler was an actor, concluded one, he was an actor who believed in the part.

Still, thanks to the complexity of our minds, we need not be perpetual dupes of our own chicanery. The mind has many parts, some designed for virtue, some designed for reason, some clever enough to outwit the parts that are neither. One self may deceive another, but every now and then a third self sees the truth.

POCKET PENGUINS

1. Lady Chatterley's Trial
2. **Eric Schlosser** Cogs in the Great Machine
3. **Nick Hornby** Otherwise Pandemonium
4. **Albert Camus** Summer in Algiers
5. **P. D. James** Innocent House
6. **Richard Dawkins** The View from Mount Improbable
7. **India Knight** On Shopping
8. **Marian Keyes** Nothing Bad Ever Happens in Tiffany's
9. **Jorge Luis Borges** The Mirror of Ink
10. **Roald Dahl** A Taste of the Unexpected
11. **Jonathan Safran Foer** The Unabridged Pocketbook of Lightning
12. **Homer** The Cave of the Cyclops
13. **Paul Theroux** Two Stars
14. **Elizabeth David** Of Pageants and Picnics
15. **Anaïs Nin** Artists and Models
16. **Antony Beevor** Christmas at Stalingrad
17. **Gustave Flaubert** The Desert and the Dancing Girls
18. **Anne Frank** The Secret Annexe
19. **James Kelman** Where I Was
20. **Hari Kunzru** Noise
21. **Simon Schama** The Bastille Falls
22. **William Trevor** The Dressmaker's Child
23. **George Orwell** In Defence of English Cooking
24. **Michael Moore** Idiot Nation
25. **Helen Dunmore** Rose, 1944
26. **J. K. Galbraith** The Economics of Innocent Fraud
27. **Gervase Phinn** The School Inspector Calls
28. **W. G. Sebald** Young Austerlitz
29. **Redmond O'Hanlon** Borneo and the Poet
30. **Ali Smith** Ali Smith's Supersonic 70s
31. **Sigmund Freud** Forgetting Things
32. **Simon Armitage** King Arthur in the East Riding
33. **Hunter S. Thompson** Happy Birthday, Jack Nicholson
34. **Vladimir Nabokov** Cloud, Castle, Lake
35. **Niall Ferguson** 1914: Why the World Went to War

POCKET PENGUINS

36. **Muriel Spark** The Snobs
37. **Steven Pinker** Hotheads
38. **Tony Harrison** Under the Clock
39. **John Updike** Three Trips
40. **Will Self** Design Faults in the Volvo 760 Turbo
41. **H. G. Wells** The Country of the Blind
42. **Noam Chomsky** Doctrines and Visions
43. **Jamie Oliver** Something for the Weekend
44. **Virginia Woolf** Street Haunting
45. **Zadie Smith** Martha and Hanwell
46. **John Mortimer** The Scales of Justice
47. **F. Scott Fitzgerald** The Diamond as Big as the Ritz
48. **Roger McGough** The State of Poetry
49. **Ian Kershaw** Death in the Bunker
50. **Gabriel García Márquez** Seventeen Poisoned Englishmen
51. **Steven Runciman** The Assault on Jerusalem
52. **Sue Townsend** The Queen in Hell Close
53. **Primo Levi** Iron Potassium Nickel
54. **Alistair Cooke** Letters from Four Seasons
55. **William Boyd** Protobiography
56. **Robert Graves** Caligula
57. **Melissa Bank** The Worst Thing a Suburban Girl Could Imagine
58. **Truman Capote** My Side of the Matter
59. **David Lodge** Scenes of Academic Life
60. **Anton Chekhov** The Kiss
61. **Claire Tomalin** Young Bysshe
62. **David Cannadine** The Aristocratic Adventurer
63. **P. G. Wodehouse** Jeeves and the Impending Doom
64. **Franz Kafka** The Great Wall of China
65. **Dave Eggers** Short Short Stories
66. **Evelyn Waugh** The Coronation of Haile Selassie
67. **Pat Barker** War Talk
68. **Jonathan Coe** 9th & 13th
69. **John Steinbeck** Murder
70. **Alain de Botton** On Seeing and Noticing